Let's Learn About

BIRDS

A Fun-to-Learn Activity Book

Written by
Carolyn Marino

Illustrated by
Jill Osborne

Watermill Press

Birds of a Feather

A bird is an animal with feathers and wings.
There are many kinds of birds.
Color these six birds. Two are the same.
Can you circle them?

Mothers & Babies

Chickens and ducks are birds. So are penguins.
Can you draw a line from these mother birds to
their babies?   Now color all the birds.

chicken

duckling

duck

penguin chicks

penguin

chicks

What a Pretty Bird!

This bird is pretty. Find his beak and color it yellow. Find the branch he is sitting on. Color it brown and color the leaves green. Find his legs and color them gray. Find his wing and tail and color them black. Color the rest of him red.

Scarlet Tanager

Up, Up and Away!

Birds are covered with feathers. Feathers are very light. If you blow on a feather, it will float in the air. Feathers help birds fly. They also keep birds warm.

Circle the things that fly.

wagon

jet

hot-air balloon

spaceship

cherries

flower

bird

truck

Who Cannot Fly?

All birds have wings and feathers. But some birds, like the ostrich, cannot fly. Do you know who else cannot fly?

Connect the dots to find out.

Home, Tweet, Home

Birds live in many places—forests, fields, water.
Even in your backyard or inside your house.

Can you draw a line from these birds to where they live?

duck

parakeet

penguin

finch

pond

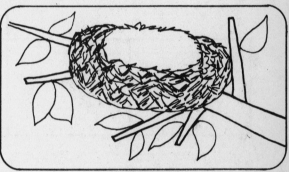

nest in tree

cage

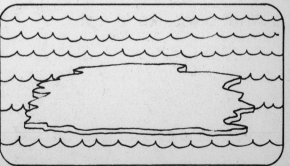

ice

Wing It!

Read the clues below. Then fill in the letters in each box.

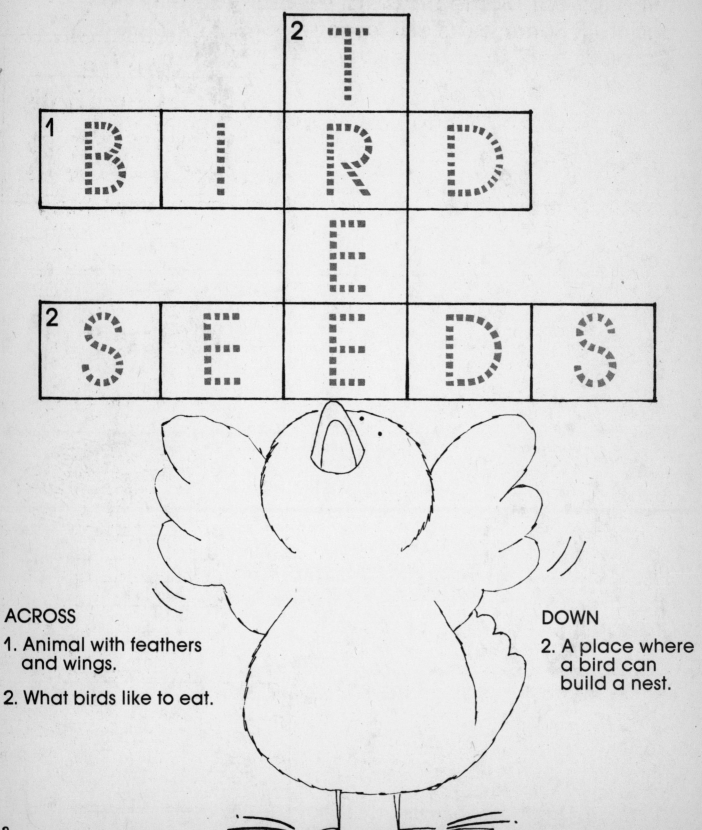

ACROSS

1. Animal with feathers and wings.

2. What birds like to eat.

DOWN

2. A place where a bird can build a nest.

What's For Dinner?

Different kinds of birds like different things to eat. Some birds eat seeds and fruit. Some birds eat insects. Big birds eat fish or mice.

Circle the things you would feed a bird.

Charlie Cardinal's **DINER**

berries

spaghetti

seeds

bug

lollipop

worms

soup

Rhyme & Color

This chickadee likes to eat bugs.
Circle the words that rhyme with **bug**.
Then color all the pictures.

horse

jug

hat

pen

rug

tug

mug

top

Hmmmm!

Hummingbirds can fly quickly or slowly, forward or backward. They eat the nectar from flowers.

This little hummingbird only likes flowers with five petals. Circle them for her. Then write the number 5:

5

Lots of Eggs

Every bird hatches from an egg. The baby bird pecks a hole in the shell with its sharp beak. The shell cracks. Out comes the baby bird.
Birds' eggs can be big or little. They can be blue, green, red, gray or brown. Sometimes they have spots on them. Here are some eggs.

Color three eggs blue.
Color two eggs green.
Color five eggs red.
Color one egg brown.
Color four eggs gray.

Which Comes First?

This chick is hatching from its shell.
Put a number 1 on the picture that comes first.
Put a number 2 on the picture that comes next.
Put a number 3 on the picture that comes after number 2.
Put a number 4 on the picture that comes last.

Who Is Hungry?

Most birds are good mothers and fathers. They keep the baby birds warm in the nest and feed them.

Mother and father are feeding their hungry babies. Count all the worms you see.
Then color the picture.

WORMS

Which Way?

Baby bird is trying to fly. He wiggles and wiggles. Oops! He fell out of the nest. Can you help him find his way back in? Follow the ABC's from A to Z.

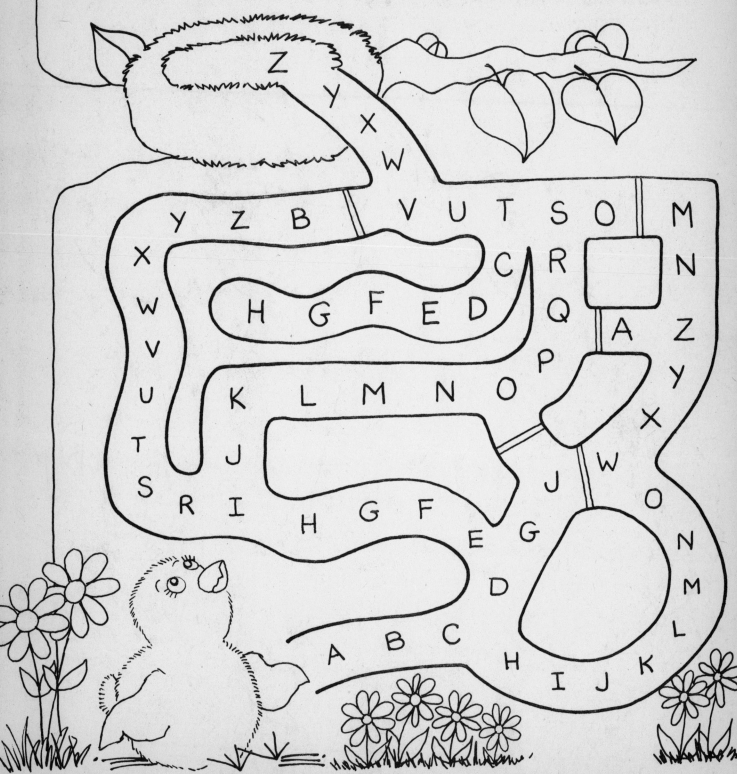

Who Is the Biggest?

The biggest bird is the ostrich.
The ostrich is also the fastest runner.
Circle the biggest ostrich.
Now color all the ostriches.

Who Is the Smallest?

The smallest bird is the bee hummingbird. Its nest is very small. The nest is the size of half a walnut shell. Circle the smallest hummingbird. Now color all the hummingbirds.

Clever Crow

Some people say the crow is the smartest bird. Crows are so smart that scarecrows don't fool them.

Look at these scarecrows. Circle the one that is different.

Where Are the Birds?

Birds escape from their enemies by flying away.
Some little birds fluff out their feathers and hiss. Some birds
have feathers that are the colors of their homes.
That makes it hard for their enemies to see them.

How many birds are hiding in this picture? Color all the
birds you can find.

Which Way?

When the weather gets cold, some birds fly away to where it is warm. Then they fly home again. This little bird is lost. He can't find his way home. Can you help him?

START

FINISH

Home Tweet Home

Peter's Puzzle

Some birds can learn to talk. Peter Parrot can talk. But he can only say words that start with the letter P. Color the things that Peter can say.

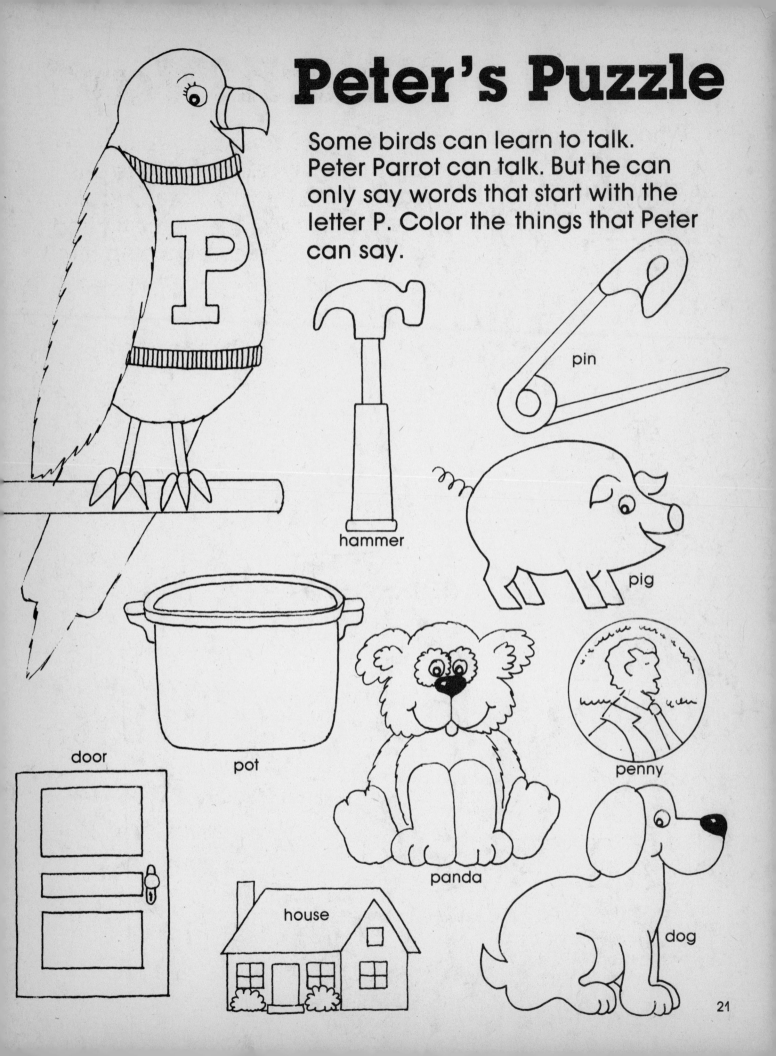

pin

hammer

pig

door

pot

penny

panda

house

dog

Can You See It?

"Whoo," says the owl. He is worried. He has lost his glasses. Can you find them? Color his glasses red.

Color By Numbers

This is a toucan. Would you like to color him?

Color the 1 yellow.
Color the 2's orange.
Color the 3's red.
Color the 4's blue.
Color the 5's green.
Color the 6's brown.
Color the 7's gray.
Color the 8's black.

The toucan's throat is white.

Proud as a Peacock

This beautiful bird is a peacock. How many tail feathers does he have? Write the number on the lines below. Then color all his feathers.

Bath Time

Birds like water. This blue jay wants to dive into a bird bath. Circle the birdbath with the fewest birds in it.

Match the Feet

This little duck has been swimming.
Now he wants to go for a walk.
What do his feet look like?
Circle them.

Knock on Wood

The bird hiding in the tree likes to peck holes in wood. He is a woodpecker. Follow the dots to see him.

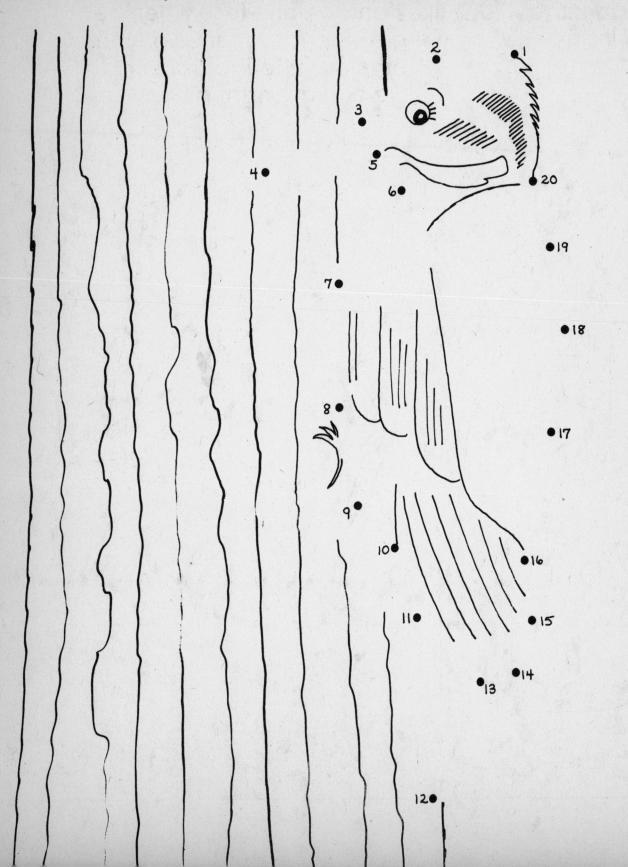

In the Pink

This bird lives in a swamp. His legs look like stilts. He likes to stand on one leg. When he gets tired, he stands on the other leg. He is a flamingo. Color him bright pink.

Flamingo

All Mixed-Up

This silly nuthatch likes to walk up the tree backward.

This word is backward. Can you fix it?

SDRIB

Write the letters in the correct order below:

_____ _____ _____ _____ _____

Answer Page

Page 3: chicken—chicks
duck—duckling
penguin—penguin chicks

Page 5: The jet, spaceship, hot-air balloon and bird fly.

Page 7: duck—pond
parakeet—cage
penguin—ice
finch—nest in tree

Page 9: What's For Dinner?

Berries, seeds, a bug and worms are for dinner.

Page 10: Jug, rug, tug and mug rhyme with **bug**.

Page 13: Which Comes First?

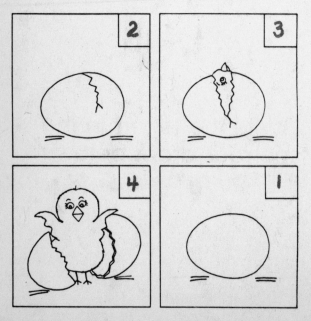

Page 14: There are 14 hidden worms.

Page 15: Which Way?

Page 19: There are 10 hidden birds.

Page 20: Which Way?

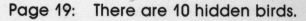

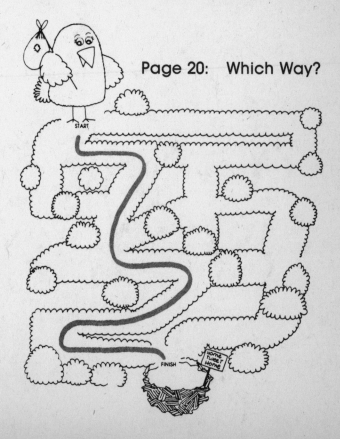

Answer Page

Page 21: Peter the Parrot can say pig, pin, pot, panda and penny.

Page 24: The peacock has 11 tail feathers.

Page 25: Bath Time

Page 26: Match the Feet

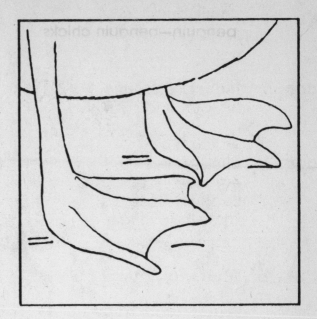

Page 29: <u>B</u> <u>I</u> <u>R</u> <u>D</u> <u>S</u>

You can draw your favorite bird in the space below.

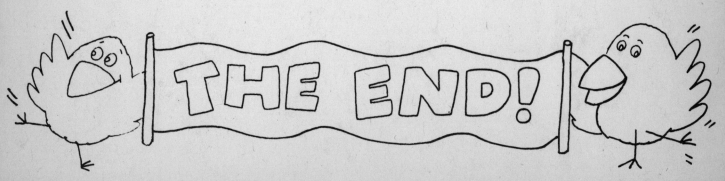